CONTENTS

Pedigree®

Published 2012. Pedigree Books Ltd, Beech Hill House, Walnut Gardens, Exeter, Devon EX4 4DH
books@pedigreegroup.co.uk www.pedigreebooks.com
The Pedigree trademark, email and website addresses, are the sole and exclusive properties of Pedigree Group Limited,
used under licence in this publication.

SPEND A YEAR WITH BUILD·A·BEAR WORKSHOP®

hi friend!

The new 2013 Annual is packed full of fun tips to help you cele-bear-ate every special occasion this year. There are colouring pages, recipes, make-its galore and ideas for hosting bearrific parties for your friends and family.

So, put a pen in your paw, turn the page and go fur it!

BEAREMY® AND PAWLETTE COUFUR®

£7.99

BIRTHDAYS

BEARY HAPPY BIRTHDAY

There's always a reason to pawty – and none better than a birthday.

Over the next few pages you'll find a step-by-step guide to throwing a party to remembear. Planning everything from pawfect party invites to games and snacks. There's also a beautiful cake to bake with a grown-up's help, of course.

I love birthdays because...

Cele-bear-ate the good stuff!

HOW TO HOST A
BUILD·A·BEAR WORKSHOP®
SLEEPOVER

Begin by making a list of friends (and their furry friends). Then use the opposite page to compile the ultimate guest list. Remember to first ask your parents how many friends you can invite. You can tick the boxes once your friends have replied to your invites. Don't forget to remind them to bring a furry friend along!

A friend is a present you give yourself!

BUILD·A·BEAR WORKSHOP®

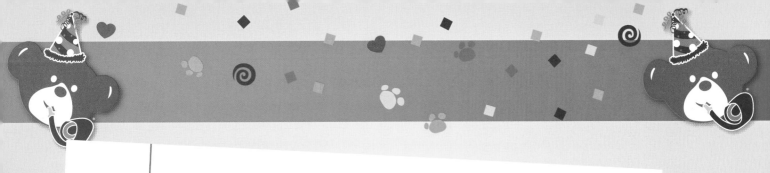

my best bear-loving buddies are:

1. ....

2. ....

3. ....

4. ....

5. ....

The furry friend they're bringing is named:

1. ....

2. ....

3. ....

4. ....

5. ....

BEARY CREATIVE INVITES

Invites set the tone for any party, so give yours a snoozy sleepover theme!

here's what you do...

Ask a grown-up to take a photo of you and your furry friend. You could even wear your pyjamas!

Get a copy of the picture printed – one for each of your guests.

Copy one of the two messages on the opposite page onto white paper. Photocopy it so you have a copy for each picture.

Cut out the message and glue it onto the back of the photo.

Dear _____

I'm having a sleepover,
Hope you can come.
Please bring a bear buddy,
We'll have tons of fun!

Date:
Times:
Address:
RSVP to:

Dear _____

My birthday is coming,
It would be divine,
If you and your teddy
Could sleepover at mine!

Date:
Times:
Address:
RSVP to:

PAWFECT PAWTY GAMES

Sleepovers are not all about catching zzzz's! You and your guests will have plenty of time for fun before lights out. Check out these ideas...

WHAT'S THE TIME MISTER BEAR?

- Pick a person to be Mister Bear.
- He or she stands at one end of the room or garden with their back turned to everyone else.
- The others ask 'What's the time Mister Bear?' and Mister Bear picks any time and tells them – i.e. 'It's 5 o'clock'.
- Everyone must take the same number of steps towards Mister Bear – so 5 o'clock equals 5 steps.
- The group then asks again, Mister Bear may say '3 o'clock' and everyone takes 3 steps.
- At any point when asked the time Mister Bear can shout 'Dinner Time' and turn and chase the group. Obviously this becomes more exciting the closer the group is to Mister Bear.
- The person caught by Mister Bear then becomes the new Mister Bear.

COUNT THE CUBS

- Ask a grown-up to buy you a small bag and a big bag of jelly bear-shaped sweets.
- Ask the adult to count the bear sweets from the big bag into a large jar and write down the count.
- Each party guest has a go at guessing how many are in the jar.
- The guest whose guess is closest wins the small bag of jelly bears as a prize.

BEARYOKE

- Pick a pile of CDs and grab your stereo.
- Take turns serenading your bear with your favourite song - you could even do a growly duet!

WE'RE GOING ON A BEAR HUNT

- Once you've played Count The Cubs, this is a great way of using up the sweets.
- Give each colour bear sweet a value – i.e. red bear = 1 point, yellow bear = 2 points.
- Ask a grown-up to hide the sweets throughout the house and/or garden.
- You then all have 10 minutes to track down as many bears as possible.
- At the count-up the winner is the person whose sweets add up to the highest value.

FURRY HIDE -N- SEEK

- Nominate one guest to be the seeker.
- The other guests all have to hide themselves (with their bear for company) in nooks, crannies and cubby holes.
- The seeker has to try to find all the hiders and their furry friends.
- If the seeker is stumped, guests are allowed to hint at their whereabouts by growling softly.

BALLOON BEARS

Give a nod to your favourite furry chum with this brilliant balloon bear. Your party guests will love creating them and playing with them.

here's what you do....

- One orange balloon per person (blown up)
- Several sheets of stiff coloured paper in orange, blue and white
- Permanent black marker pen
- One orange, black or brown coloured pom-pom per person
- PVA glue
- Scissors

2 Starting at the edge of the orange card, draw 2 semi-circlular ear shapes, one beside the other. Cut these out. Now cut smaller semi circles for the inner ear from either the blue or white card.

1 Draw two large circles on the white card – you could draw round an upturned egg cup. Then draw two smaller circles on the blue card – draw around a 2p piece. Cut the four circles out and draw a large black spot in the centre of each of the blue circles using black pen. Stick the blue circles onto the white circles as shown.

3 Next, squidge blobs of glue onto the balloon where the eyes, nose and ears will go.

4 Stick the pre-made eyes on. Glue the folded edge of the ears to the balloon so the ears stick up at right angles and add the red pom-pom nose.

5 Finally, add the bear's mouth using your black marker pen.

TiME FOR BED WiTH YOUR TED

Yawn! It's getting late, but before you snuggle up with your BFFs – that's Bear Friend Forever – it's time to relax and get cosy.

Here are some yummy snacks to help you and your guests have a good night's sleep.

Honey Milk

- Measure out a mug of cold milk per guest.
- Tip the milk from all the mugs into a pan and warm on the stove or hob – don't let it boil, though.
- Add a dash of cinnamon and a teaspoon of honey and stir.
- Share the bear milk between the mugs.

French Teddy Toast

- Beat 3 eggs in a wide-rimmed bowl with 1/4 cup milk, 3 tablespoons of honey and a pinch of nutmeg.
- Dip a slice of white bread into the bowl and leave for 1 minute until soaked, turn it over and repeat so that both sides have soaked up the mixture. The mixture should be enough for 6 – 8 slices.
- Pre-heat a frying pan or griddle with a knob of butter.
- When each slice is coated, place it in the pan until golden brown on both sides.

Peaceful Porridge

Not just for mornings – porridge is yummy made with warm milk and a teaspoon of honey stirred in for good measure.

PAWS FOR THOUGHT!
Knives are sharp and ovens are hot. Always ask a parent or grown-up to help in the kitchen!

Fruits of the Forage Salad

Bears love foraging for fruit in the forest. Chop and mix together slices of banana, halved cherries and chunks of watermelon in a bowl.

Beary Tall Tales

Once you're snuggled up tight, it's time for a bedtime story. Can you make up some fun tales involving the totally bearilliant adventures of your own furry friends?

You could start with an old favourite like 'Goldilocks and the Three Bears', or give a rendition of 'We're Going on a Bear Hunt' and act out the story using your own furry friends.

Or, perhaps your furry friends could be swashbuckling bears on the high seas or brave bears mounted on dazzling white steeds rescuing fair bear princesses. Where will your imagination take you - and them?

furry friend cake

This fab creation is actually a simple sponge with buttercream icing.

It's beary easy to bake and so scrummy – you can even munch the marzipan bear on the top!

here's what you do....

1 Preheat the oven to 180 °C / gas mark 4.

2 Measure all the ingredients out into a large bowl.

YOU WILL NEED:

For the cake:
- 225g self raising flour
- 225g unsalted butter
- 225g caster sugar
- 4 eggs
- 2 teaspoons baking powder
- A few drops of vanilla essence
- Zest of half a lemon

For the icing:
- 140g/5oz. softened butter
- 280g/10 oz. icing sugar
- 1 tablespoon milk

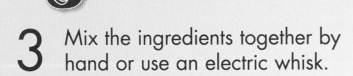

3 Mix the ingredients together by hand or use an electric whisk.

PAWS FOR THOUGHT!
Knives are sharp and ovens are hot. Always ask a parent or grown-up to help in the kitchen!

5 Place them on the middle shelf of the oven for 15–25 minutes – or until golden brown. When cooked a knife stuck into the middle should come out clean.

4 Pour the mixture into two pre-greased non-stick 18cm (7 inch) tins.

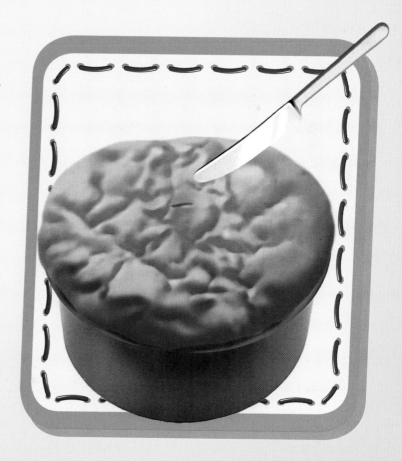

6 Cool on a wire rack.

Furry Friend Cake

Now you've made the yummy cake, it's time to bring your bear to life. He looks so cute, doesn't he? You'll need a grown-up's helping hand with this part.

here's what you do....

1 Pinch a chunk of golden marzipan from the pack and roll it into a ball a little larger than a golf ball.

2 For his head, take a smaller chunk and roll a slightly smaller ball. Pinch two small portions of golden marzipan for the ears and two tiny balls of white marzipan to make the eyes.

YOU WILL NEED:

For the bears:
- 1 pack golden marzipan
- 1 pack white marzipan
- Black icing pen or black food colouring and a fine paint brush
- Bowl of water

3 Pinch four small-ish balls and roll them to make the arms and legs.

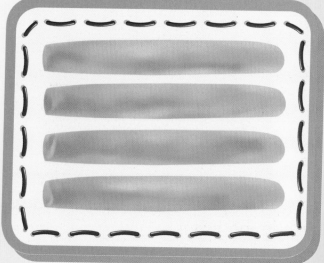

4 Push the eyes and ears onto the head – using a little water to help them stick together.

20

5 Use the end of the paintbrush to put a dint in each ear, and a line for a smiling mouth.

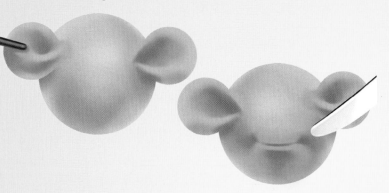

6 Using black food colouring or a black icing pen, create the pupils of the eyes and the nose.

7 Stick the limbs to the body and then stick on the head. Use the end of the paintbrush again to make dints in the paws.

8 Your bear is finished. You could always make him a pal or two with any remaining marzipan! Now all you need to do is ice your cake.

Now make the buttercream icing

- Mix the icing sugar and butter in a bowl until smooth and ice the now cooled cake.

- Spread a little under half the mixture on the bottom layer of the cake using the flat side of a knife or a spatula.

- Place the top layer on the bottom layer.

- Use the remaining icing to ice the top of the cake.

- Put your marzipan bear on top.

21

DESIGN-A-DRESS

This furry friend is off to a Birthday Bash!
Can you design her a knockout frock to wow her pals, using your best colouring pens or pencils?

SPOT THE DIFFERENCE

This bear is busy planning her birthday sleepover and is on the phone telling her BFF all about the fun they're going to have. Can you spot and circle five differences between picture A and picture B? You'll need to look carefully, some of the changes are bearly visible!

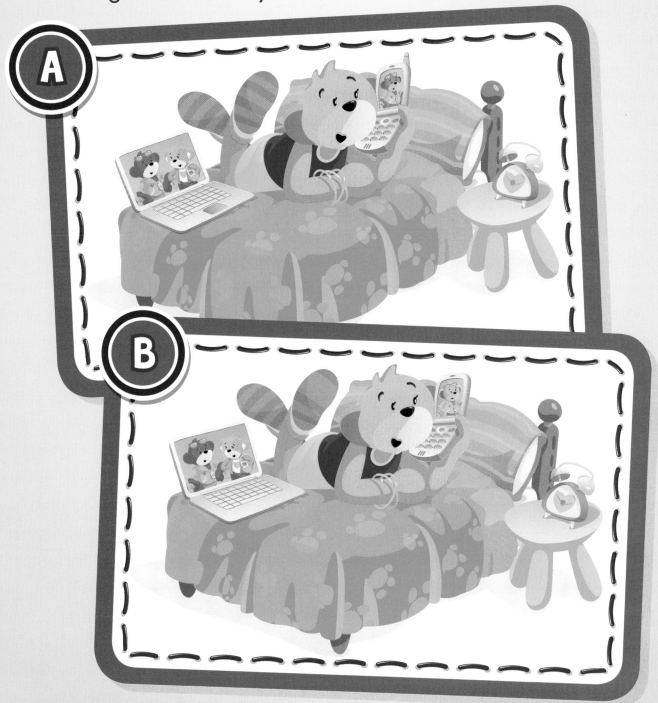

Find the answers on page 76.

VALENTINE'S DAY

BEAR YOUR HEART

Bears are measured by the size of their hearts and Valentine's Day is the pawfect opportunity to show the beary special people in your life just how much they mean to you.

In this super section you'll find a Valentine's Day Card to make for someone you love. So put your best paw forward and start by thinking about all the special people in your life. Friends, parents, grandparents, uncles, the family pet and of course your furry friend... Write them all down, along with the things you love most about them. Then give everyone on your list a big bear hug!

I LOVE _ _ _ _ _ _ _ _ _ _ _ _ _ _

BECAUSE _ _ _ _ _ _ _ _ _ _ _

_ _ _ _ _ _ _ _ _ _ _ _ _ _

_ _ _ _ _ _ _ _ _ _ _ _ _

I LOVE _ _ _ _ _ _ _ _ _ _ _ _ _

BECAUSE _ _ _ _ _ _ _ _ _ _ _

_ _ _ _ _ _ _ _ _ _ _ _ _ _

_ _ _ _ _ _ _ _ _ _ _ _ _ _

I LOVE _ _ _ _ _ _ _ _ _ _ _ _

BECAUSE _ _ _ _ _ _ _ _ _ _

_ _ _ _ _ _ _ _ _ _ _ _ _ _

_ _ _ _ _ _ _ _ _ _ _ _ _

I LOVE _ _ _ _ _ _ _ _ _ _ _

BECAUSE _ _ _ _ _ _ _ _ _ _

_ _ _ _ _ _ _ _ _ _ _ _ _

_ _ _ _ _ _ _ _ _ _ _ _ _

Bears who are loved are bears in luck

CUTE CARD

Bear your heart to a friend or loved one with this cute and cuddly Valentine's Day card.

It's simple to make and simply gorgeous to give!

here's what you do...

1 Take the A4 piece of white card and fold carefully in half widthways, to make an A5 card. Now follow the instructions opposite, to draw a bear for the front of the card.

2 With a pencil, draw two circles. A big one for the body and a smaller one for the head. Just like the image below.

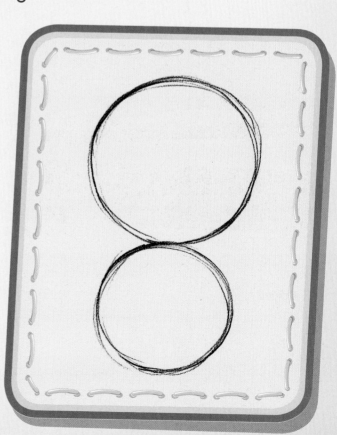

3 Add two circles for the ears and another for the snout.

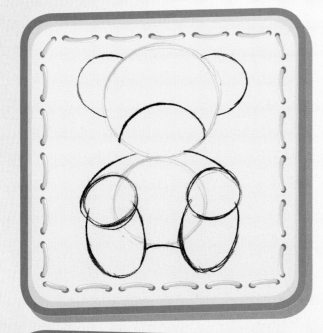

4 Now add the details - the eyes, nose, mouth and paws. You should see your bear taking shape before your eyes!

5 Go over the outline in black pen then colour in his fur with light and dark brown felt pens.

BEAR iN MiND!

It's a good idea to practice drawing the bear on a piece of scrap paper first. Then sketch lightly with the pencil when drawing your bear on the card, so you can rub out mistakes. You can always go over the lines once you're sure they look pawfect.

now to make the card

So, you've designed your card. Now it's time to add the all important greeting inside. Will you sign your name or remain an anonymous sender?

here's what you do...

1 Colour your bear in using the light and dark brown and black pens and decorate the rest of the card with little hearts – you could draw and colour these red, or use heart-shaped stickers or jewels.

2 Stick the adhesive googly eyes over the bear's eyes.

3 Draw a large heart on the red card. Stick this inside the card.

4 Write one of the two phrases below on the heart and sign with your name.

you're Beary special!

A big bear hug!

A Big Bear Hug!

29

TANGLE TRAIL

This bunny loves balloons and her favourite colour is pink. Can you help her work out which of her friends is holding the red balloon?

Write your answer here

Find the answers on page 76.

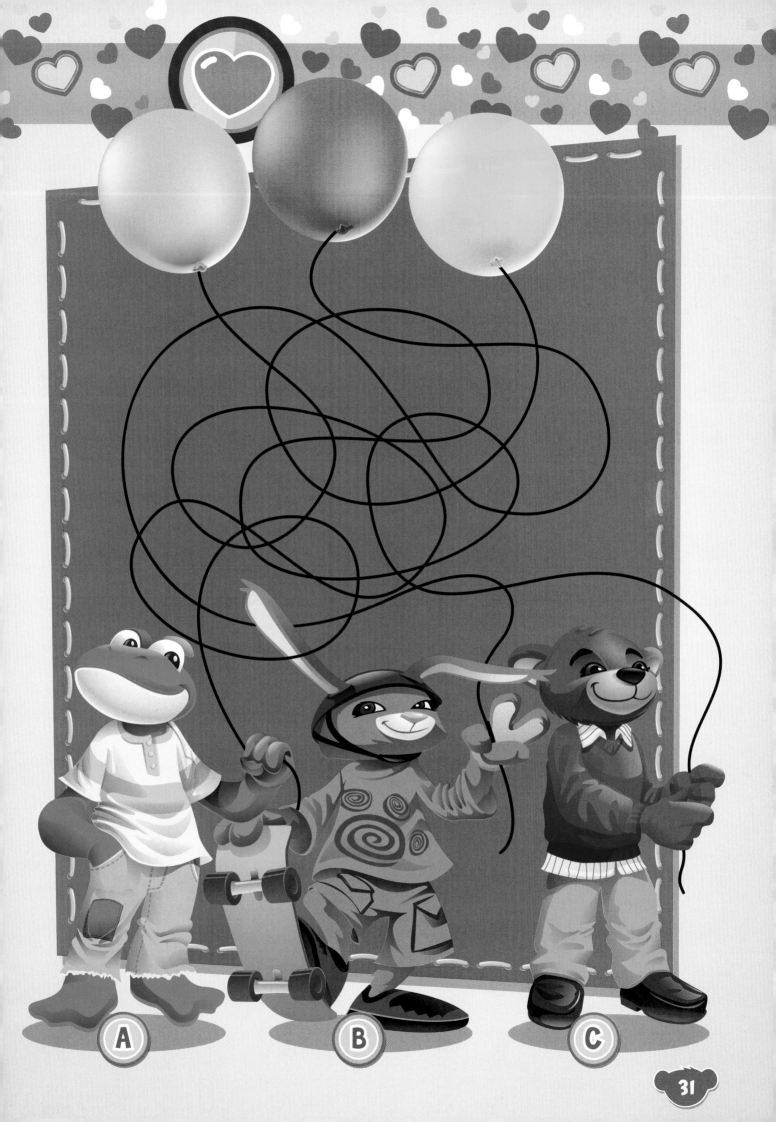

31

EASTER

hop into spring

Ah, springtime! Season of new beginnings. Trees blossom, flowers poke their cheery heads from the earth and sleepy creatures emerge from their long winter sleep. Bears and bunnies love the spring and feel lively and energetic at this time of year. Do you? Use the page opposite to write down all the pawsitive things you are looking forward to doing with your BFF this spring – that's bear friend forever.

Spring also means it's time to cele-bear-ate Easter. So in this section you'll learn how to create an cool chick card and organise a brilliant Easter egg hunt. How egg-straordinarily egg-citing!

spring makes me want to...

The beary best is yet to come!

Eye-catching Eggs

Easter Eggs are so pretty, aren't they? Decorate the egg on the opposite page using your brightest colours. You could even use glitter or glitter pens, and snippets of coloured ribbon for the bow.

Sometimes eggs are hollow and hold surprises. What would you like to find inside yours this year?

What I'd love to find in the middle of my egg is...

HOST A HUNT

Easter Egg Hunts are furbulous fun, so why not ask a grown-up if you can organise one for your friends or neighbours? Here are some ideas:

TRAIL BY TORCHLIGHT

An evening egg hunt is super fun. Invite your guests at twilight. Give them a mug of scrummy hot chocolate and a torch and let them loose in the house or garden.

Rhyming Clues

Instead of hiding lots of small eggs, buy one large egg per guest and make a trail of clues, which will lead the guest to another clue and eventually to the egg. You can make the trail as long or as short as you like.

As for the eggs, you could hide them all separately and send each guest on a different trail to his or her egg. Or give 2 groups a trail each, with clues leading to a bumper crop of eggs at the end. It's even more fun to make the clues rhyme.

For example:
To find the next clue, be sure to use your head, it's at the bottom garden, hidden somewhere in the ____!

So the guest would head for the garden shed where they'd find another clue, and so on.

Colour-Coded Chase

This is a great way to ensure there are no squabbles over which eggs belong to whom. Give each guest a coloured sticker with their name on and tell them to look out for eggs wrapped in that colour foil.

It's Got Your Name On It...

Another way to spice things up is to stick a nametag on each egg and tell each guest to hunt only for the egg with his or her name on it.
The first to find their named egg claims a bonus prize – which could be an additional egg for example, or a bag of sweets.

Cold, Cold, Warmer...

Get the guests to hunt in turn for their egg and give them helpful clues like, 'cool, cold, warm, getting warmer and hot', to let them know if they're way off track or about to stumble on their egg.

COOL CHICK CARD

This little chick is delivering a chirpy Easter message. If you look closely, you and the person who receives your card will see he is extra special, because he's made from part of you.

here's what you do....

1 Draw a large oval (egg-shape) onto the yellow card in pencil. It should be at least as tall as your hand from palm to fingertips.

2 Trace around your hands with the pencil onto the second piece of yellow card. Cut out the hand shapes.

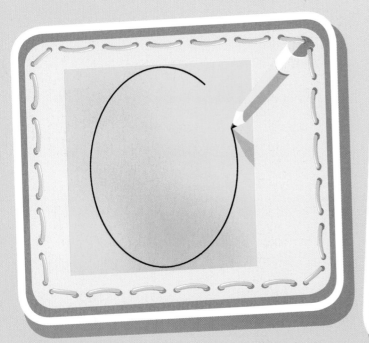

Happy Easter

3 Attach a hand 'wing' – fingers down to each side of the oval body with a paper fastener.

4 Now draw two leg shapes and a diamond for the beak onto the orange card. Cut out and fold the diamond in half to give a beak shape. Stick legs and beak onto body.

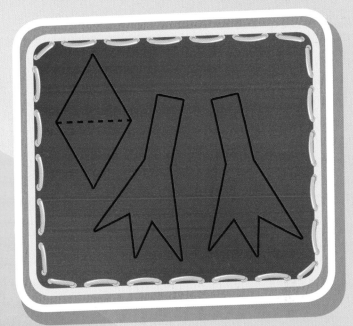

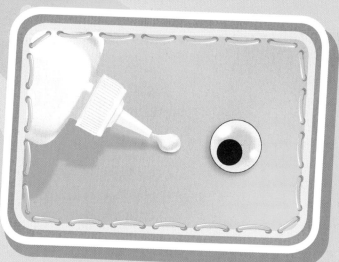

5 Stick googly eyes in place or draw eyes on using black pen. Use pen to write your Easter message on your chick's tummy!

BOX THE BEAR

Find a friend to play this game with you. The youngest begins. Then, take it in turns to join two dots together horizontally or vertically using a pen or pencil.

When your line completes a box, write your initials inside it and have another turn.
You get a point for each initialed square.

If the box also contains a bear, you get two points.
The winner is the person with the most points.

DOT-TO-DOT

This puppy's got a spring in his step. Can you join the dots to find out what he's doing?

SUMMER HOLIDAYS

STEP into SUMMER

This summer is going to be absolutely awesome!

Read on for brilliant ways to spend your days. There are tips on hosting a totally cool pool party in your garden – even if you don't have a swimming pool! Plus, there are ideas to get you moving and activities to help make even a rainy day fun!

This summer I'm totally going to...

hang out with _ _ _ _ _ _ _ _ _ _ _
_ _ _ _ _ _ _ _ _ _ _ _ _ _ _ _ _ _

play _ _ _ _ _ _ _ _ _ _ _ _ _ _ _ _

visit _ _ _ _ _ _ _ _ _ _ _ _ _ _ _ _

learn to _ _ _ _ _ _ _ _ _ _ _ _ _ _

go on a day trip to _ _ _ _ _ _ _ _
_ _ _ _ _ _ _ _ _ _ _ _ _ _ _ _ _ _

go on holiday to _ _ _ _ _ _ _ _ _ _
with _ _ _ _ _ _ _ _ _ _ _ _ _ _ _ _

spend time with _ _ _ _ _ _ _ _ _ _

Life is sweeter with a little honey

43

HOST A COOL POOL PARTY

Get ready for some smashing, splashing fun!

PHONE A FRIEND
Who would you love to lounge by your pool with? Write the names of your friends here and then ask a grown-up if you can phone or write to invite them.

my perfect pool pals are:

SUMMER STYLE

You'll want to look your best poolside, so pull out your most colourful swimsuit and cover-up from your wardrobe. Oh and don't forget your sunglasses, a hat or cap and sunscreen!

SPLASH DOWN

A pool party needs watery fun so ask a grown-up to pull out your paddling pool or set up a sprinkler in the garden for fountains of fun.

COOLING DRINKS AND CANAPÉS

You'll all be thirsty after splashing around so quench your thirsts with this fresh drink. Blend fresh strawberries, pineapple chunks, raspberries and a splash of lime cordial together and serve in tall glasses with lots of ice and a straw. For canapés, try tiny crackers with a dab of cool, soft cheese and a sprig of parsley or a slice of cucumber. You could even ask a grown-up to take the role of pool waiter.

45

READ ALL ABOUT IT!

Reading is great fun, so grab your fave mag or a page-turning novel and dive-in!

LOUNGERS

It's nice to be comfortable while you catch some rays. You could use deckchairs or sun loungers, or simply lay out colourful towels on the grass.

MUSIC

Do you have a personal MP3 player, a radio or stereo? Bring it out to add a soundtrack to your summer. Just remember the neighbours and keep the volume at a reasonable level.

BEAR iN MiND!

BE SUN SMART

To enjoy the sun safely you need to ask a grown-up to apply sun cream to you regularly and liberally – especially if you've been for a dip. Pop on a hat. Spend time in the shade at lunchtime or in the hottest part of the day – especially when your shadow is shorter than you!

47

GET MOVING

Use the space below to write down your favourite sport and the team or sportsperson you support or admire.

Here are some games to play in your garden or the local park:

Furry Friend Relay

Get a group of pals, pick your favourite bear and run a relay with him or her as the baton. Each sprint a leg of the garden or park and pass your furry friend swiftly and smoothly between you.

Balance game

Lay two skipping ropes or several scarves end to end to make a long 'beam' on the grass. Now practice walking on your toes along the beam without losing your balance or stepping off the beam. Chin up, look forward, arms out to the side.

French skipping

Try this quirky new way of skipping! You'll need at least two friends to play with you and a piece of strong elastic tied to form a 3 metre long loop.

- Two people are 'enders' and stand inside the loop of elastic, facing each other, feet slightly apart, with the elastic passing round the backs of their ankles.
- They move back until the elastic makes two taut lines between them.
- The jumper then jumps in, around and onto the elastic while singing a rhyme.
- If the jumper completes the rhyme without tripping, the elastic is raised to knee height (then thigh height).
- If they trip up, they swap with an ender who becomes a jumper.

Sing while you jump:

Teddy bear, teddy bear, turn around.
Teddy bear, teddy bear, touch the ground.
Teddy bear, teddy bear, do the splits.
Teddy bear, teddy bear, give a high kick.
Teddy bear, teddy bear, go upstairs.
Teddy bear, teddy bear, say your prayers.
Teddy bear, teddy bear, turn out the light.
Teddy bear, teddy bear, say good night.

Best Furry Friends Furever

The summer holidays are doubly amazing, because you get to spend extra time with your BFF. See exactly how alike you and your best (non-furry) pal are with this fun quiz.

Take a page and at each step, circle the word you like best. You can either do this at the same time – or one after the other, taking care not to cheat and look at your friend's answers. When you're done, check the bottom of the page to find out how you've done.

1. Butterflies or Ladybirds?
2. Bears or Bunnies?
3. Hearts or Stars?
4. Shopping or Chatting?
5. Basketball or Football?
6. Movies or TV?
7. Ballet or Breakdancing?
8. Dogs or Cats?
9. Guitar or Drums?
10. Pink or Purple?

1. Butterflies or Ladybirds?
2. Bears or Bunnies?
3. Hearts or Stars?
4. Shopping or Chatting?
5. Basketball or Football?
6. Movies or TV?
7. Ballet or Breakdancing?
8. Dogs or Cats?
9. Guitar or Drums?
10. Pink or Purple?

1 – 3 identical answers

On paper you seem different, but the longer you two hang out, the more in tune you're going to get.

4 – 6 identical answers

What furbulous friends you are! You're really very similar but you also have your own interests, which is just how it should be.

7 – 10 identical answers

Time to cele-bear-ate. You guys are pawfect partners. You know each other inside out, finish each other's sentences and are always there for each other.

Beach BONANZA

Bears do like to be beside the seaside! And this furry bunch just can't wait to hit the beach and cool their paws in the crystal clear water. Count how many are there. Write the number in the box below.

write your
answer here

Find the answers on page 76.

53

HALLOWEEN

hello halloween

There's a step-by-step guide to hosting a fun Halloween party for your pals, complete with spooky snacks and decorations. There's also an idea for a brilliant bear pumpkin. So turn the page – the fun starts here.

STAY SAFE WHILE TRICK OR TREATING

Can you write down a list of five rules to make sure you stay safe and have fun while being kind and respectful of your neighbours? We've started you off…

1. Only go to houses where the owners are obviously in the Halloween spirit. Look for pumpkins outside and decorations on display. This shows they won't mind you visiting.

2. Always say thank you to people who give you treats.

3. Always go with a grown-up.

4.

5.

Don't worry - be furry

CARVE-A-BEAR

As you walk around your neighbourhood, you're sure to see some amazing carved pumpkins. Why don't you top them all this year with a brilliant pumpkin bear head?

here's what you do....

1 Cut the lid of the pumpkin off using the knife or keyhole saw.

2 Scoop the flesh and seeds out using the ice cream scoop.

PAWS FOR THOUGHT!
Pumpkin carving requires very sharp tools, so always ask a grown-up to do it for you.

3 Copy the features of the picture below onto the side of the pumpkin in black marker pen. Cut the eyes, mouth and nose out to create the bear's face.

4 Cut a round slice from the butternut squash, then chop this in half to create two semi-circles for the bear's ears.

5 Poke a cocktail stick into each end of the flat side of each butternut squash ear.

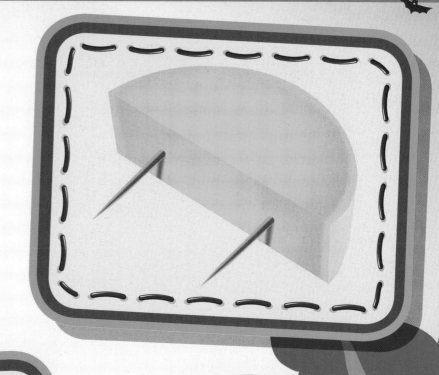

6 Decide where the ears will sit on the pumpkin and make two holes in the pumpkin for the cocktail sticks to go through – you could use a barbeque skewer to do this.

7 Sit each ear on the side of the pumpkin so that the cocktail sticks drop through the holes in the pumpkin and hold the ears in place.

8 Light the tea light and place it in the pumpkin. Put the lid on and display.

PAWS FOR THOUGHT!

Pumpkin carving requires very sharp tools, so always ask a grown-up to do it for you.

WICKED WORD SEARCH

Get in the ghostly mood with this wonderful word search. First, unjumble the anagrams below to find twelve Halloween related words. Then locate those same words hidden in the grid on the opposite page.

1.   TAB   1.

2.   STOCUME   2.

3.   STIRCK   3.

4.   REATTS   4.

5.   NIKPUMP   5.

6.   ITCHW   6.

7.   NUF   7.

8.   RIENDFS   8.

9.   KOOPSY   9.

10. TIGHN   10.

11. SHOTG   11.

12. RATPY   12.

Find the answers on page 76.

60

T	S	O	h	g	A	K	T	W	T
B	Y	B	C	E	n	O	C	E	R
T	g	y	S	O	n	U	A	E	I
R	O	F	P	n	S	I	F	T	C
E	y	R	O	I	C	T	g	E	K
A	T	I	O	K	W	K	U	h	S
T	R	E	K	P	I	g	E	m	T
S	A	n	y	m	T	P	T	D	E
Q	P	D	B	U	C	U	A	W	V
Q	h	s	M	m	P	h	J	B	U	V

61

KOOKY SPOOKY GAMES

Want to host a truly bearrific Halloween party for your chums? You'll need some kooky spooky games for your party guests.

Pumpkin Bowling:

YOU'LL NEED:

- 10 empty 2-litre fizzy drink bottles. Paint ghost faces on each and add the features with black marker pen. Put a cup of sand or small pebbles in the bottom of each, then replace the cap.
- 3 small pumpkins or squashes.

HOW TO PLAY:

1. Set the bottles up as bowling 'pins' in a triangle, 4 at the back, 3 in the middle, a row of 2, 1 at the front.
2. Divide guests into two teams.
3. Take turns at bowling over the pins with the pumpkins.
4. Keep score and each strike is rewarded with another go.

Apple Bobbing:

YOU'LL NEED:

- 2 washing up bowls
- A bag of apples
- A stopwatch

HOW TO PLAY:

1. Fill the washing up bowls with water.
2. Place the apples in the bowls, half in each.
3. Guests must duel two at a time to see who can get the most apples out with their mouths only in two minutes.

What's In The Box?

YOU'LL NEED:

- An empty cardboard box decorated with Halloween-themed gift wrap with a hole cut in one side.
- 10 spooky items to go in the box – such as a plastic spider or bat, a Halloween wig, a fake rat, an eye patch, vampire fangs, an apple, some gummy snakes, a fake eyeball, a small plastic pumpkin.
- Pieces of paper or card (one per guest) with numbers 1 – 10 written on them.

HOW TO PLAY:

1. Each person gets a card with the numbers 1–10 on.
2. They take turns putting their hand through the hole in the box and feeling the objects – they have 1 minute. Then they must go away and write down what they think they felt.
3. The winner is the person who guessed the most correctly.

SPOOKY SNACKS

Mmmm! Tea time. What superbly spooky snacks will you serve your hungry guests tonight? Check out these scrummy recipes!

Halloween Pizza

YOU WILL NEED:

- Large ready-made pizza base
- Jar of pizza sauce (or use tomato paste thinned with tbsp water)
- Block or pre-cut slices of hard mozzarella cheese
- Pumpkin, bat or ghost cookie cutter

HERE'S WHAT YOU DO:

1. Spread the pizza sauce evenly over the base.
2. Ask a grown-up to cut slices of mozzarella if not already pre-cut.
3. Take your cookie cutter and cut shapes from the cheese. Place randomly on the pizza and cook as per instructions.

Bubbling Broth

YOU WILL NEED

- Large bottle of cola
- Tub of vanilla ice cream
- Ice cube tray
- Plastic bugs

HERE'S WHAT YOU DO:

1. Fill an ice cube tray with water (you could add a small plastic bug to each).
2. Leave to freeze in the ice tray.
3. Fill glasses two thirds full with cola
4. Add a scoop of ice cream and watch it froth like a witch's brew!
4. Add ice cubes – with or without bugs!

Slimy Snake Jelly

YOU WILL NEED:

- Packs of lime or apple and cherry, grape or black currant jelly
- Gummy worms or snakes sweets
- Clear glasses or glass bowls to serve

HERE'S WHAT YOU DO:

1. Prepare the green coloured jelly as per the pack and before it sets divide it among the glasses or glass bowls, filling only halfway. Refrigerate until firm.

2. Prepare another lot of jelly in a contrasting colour – say red or blue.

3. While this is dissolving remove your glasses from the fridge and place several gummy worms or snakes on top of the set jelly in the glasses – make sure one worm hangs over the lip of the glass/bowl. Pour the second flavour of jelly over the worms, filling to the top of the glass/bowl.

4. Refrigerate and eat cold.

CHRISTMAS

BEARY MERRY CHRISTMAS

'Tis the season to be beary merry! Christmas is such a wonderful time of the year.

So turn the page to find out how to make your own beary merry Christmas wrapping paper and bake scrummy gingerbears.

my christmas wish is...

In my stocking from santa I'd
really like to find...

I can make someone else's
christmas by...

Bear in mind – Always be kind

BEARY CHRISTMAS GIFT WRAP

Sometimes the beautiful wrapping paper is just as enticing as what is in the parcel. Make your gifts look gorgeous this Christmas with this beary beautiful homemade gift wrap.

here's what you do....

1 Trace the bear head from the opposite page onto the tracing paper than transfer onto the piece of cardboard.

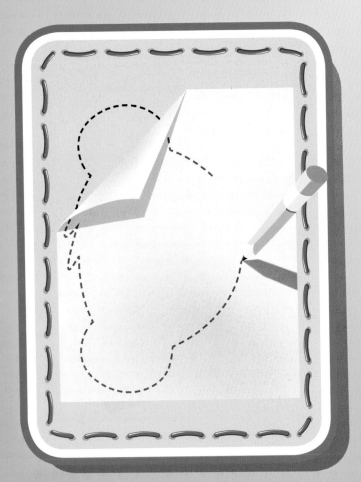

YOU WILL NEED:

- A roll of brown parcel paper
- Piece of thick cardboard
- Square of tracing paper
- Gold or silver or red paint
- Paintbrush

2 Cut out the bear head to create a cardboard template.

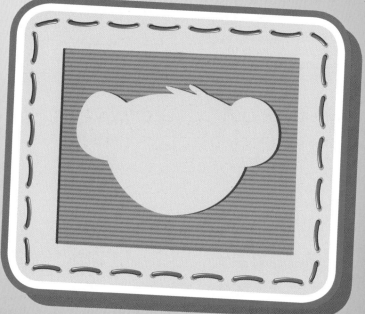

3 Roll out a section of brown paper out onto a flat surface and hold the template still against the paper.

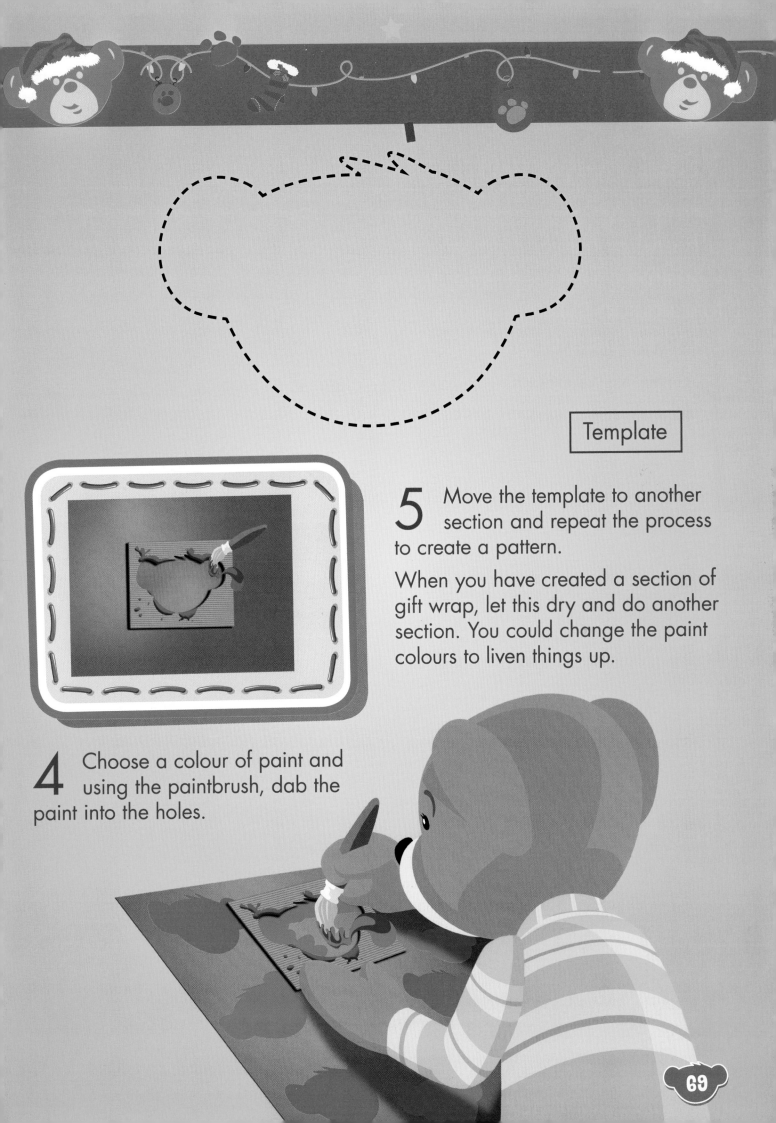

5 Move the template to another section and repeat the process to create a pattern.

When you have created a section of gift wrap, let this dry and do another section. You could change the paint colours to liven things up.

4 Choose a colour of paint and using the paintbrush, dab the paint into the holes.

TREE FOR TWO

Here's a fun game to play with a friend or family member at Christmas. The idea is to be the first to colour in the tree. Just grab some coloured pens or pencils and a dice.

how to play:

Roll the dice to see who goes first - highest number begins.

Take turns to throw the dice and colour in the part of the tree corresponding to the number you've thrown – see the key opposite.

If you've already coloured all the items corresponding to that number then miss your turn. Winner is the first to have finished the colouring.

70

colouring Key:

Throw a 1 – Colour the pot

Throw a 2 - Colour one of the small baubles

Throw a 3 – Colour one of the medium baubles

Throw a 4 – Colour one of the large baubles

Throw a 5 – Colour one of the presents

Throw a 6 – Colour the star

GINGERBEARS

Spiced, fragrant gingerbread tastes especially good at Christmas time. Try this spin on the traditional gingerbread men.

here's what you do...

1 Ask a grown-up to help and preheat oven to 180°C.

YOU WILL NEED:

- A teddy cookie or pastry cutter
- 350g plain flour
- 175g light soft brown sugar
- 100g butter
- 1 egg
- 4 tbsp. golden syrup
- 1 tsp. bicarbonate of soda
- 1½ tsps. ground ginger

2 Mix the flour, butter, ginger and bicarb in a mixing bowl with fingertips until crumbly.

PAWS FOR THOUGHT!

Ovens are hot. Always ask a parent or grown-up to help in the kitchen!

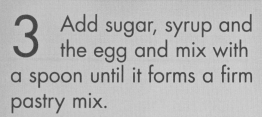

3 Add sugar, syrup and the egg and mix with a spoon until it forms a firm pastry mix.

4 Dust a rolling pin and the rolling surface with flour and roll the gingerbread out with until 5 mm thick.

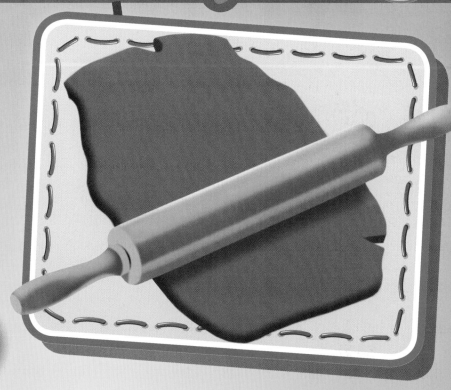

5 Cut teddy shapes with the cutter – or with a knife and place on non-stick baking tray 2cm apart to allow for spreading. Add raisins for eyes and nose.

6 Cook for 15 mins or until golden brown. Remove from tray and allow to cool on wire rack.

ROCKING RESOLUTIONS

The New Year is a time to put your best paw forward and think about all the pawsitive changes you could make.

The decision to make a change for the better is called a 'resolution'. They could be anything from tidying your room more regularly to learning to dance or vowing to try a vegetable you've never eaten before.

What are your New Year's Resolutions? And how about your furry friend? Bears are always kind and good, but maybe he or she needs to make new furry pals this year or branch out with their fashion sense? What do you think?

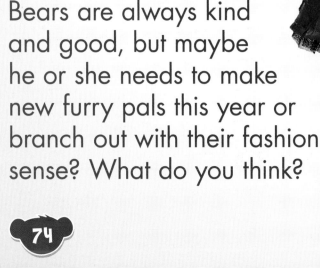

74

MY NEW YEAR'S RESOLUTIONS ARE:

MY FURRY FRIEND'S RESOLUTIONS ARE:

Everything is pawsible if you put your mind to it!

ANSWERS

Page 23
Birthdays:
SPOT THE DIFERENCE

Page 30
VALENTINE'S DAY:
TANGLE TRAIL

B – the skateboarding bunny
is her Valentine!

Page 52
SUMMER HOLIDAYS:
BEACH BONANZA

25 furry friends are heading
for the beach.

Page 60
HALLOWEEN:
WICKED WORD SEARCH

1. BAT
2. COSTUME
3. TRICKS
4. TREATS
5. PUMPKIN
6. WITCH
7. FUN
8. FRIENDS
9. SPOOKY
10. NIGHT
11. GHOST
12. PARTY

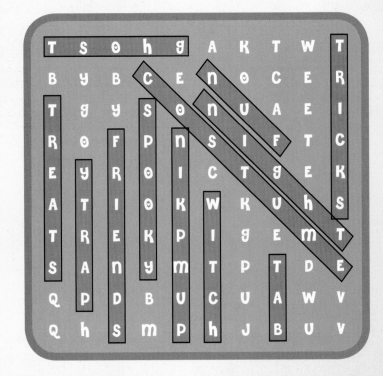

The fur may fade but the friendship lasts forever!
SEE YOU SOON!